uard thè sleep of d'Anna Fort...

...he title roles of "Hansel & G...

Iansel & Gret... ıot for kid...

*HANSEL AND GRETEL — Opera by Engelber...
mperdinck, presented by Opera New England,
...ah Caldwell, artistic director, in Sandwich Friday
...ht.*

...Richard Dyer
...be Staff

SANDWICH — "Hansel and Gretel," by the real En-
...t Humperdinck is opera's answer to "The
...ker" and Christmas Pops, and Sarah Caldwell is
... around as a Christmas goodie to all the cities on
... a New England circuit.

...dren love the catchy songs... ...attered
... the score, though one wonder... ...netimes
...eal response is to the parts of t... ...ic that
...y by the man who wrote out... ...estral
...gner's "Parsifal" and ser... ...stage
... its premiere. Usually dir... ...ivert
...n musical longeurs to... ...sing
...ge. And Sarah Caldwell... ...hen
...ention, certainly gav... ...he
...f all ages a lot to... ...ng

...w in this is the set...
...elight in color an...
...comic ingenuity,...
... the set is the...
...Gretel are disco...
...m-maker's hut...
...into children;...
...otectively gl...
...gh to eat. Fa...
...hers –...

...ed by the acoustics of the Sandwic...
...rium into Wagnerian amplitude, w...
...score's weight and lilt, and the p...
And the cast was by-and-large de...
...tunato, nicely awkward in mov...
...glamorous in tone for Hansel,...
...Gretel with charm and lucid to...
...Wotan, who brought great reson...
...father, Eunice Alberts, having a grea...
...up as the Witch, though the part lie...
...her. Victoria Vergera was less success...
...and Ellen McLain offset sweetness of s...
...whiney connections between sounds...
...how many of these performers are loca...
...which is a good step for Opera New E...
...taking — remember Elisabeth Phinney's...
...Fiordiligi a few years back, heard only on the...
...an inferior artist sang the role in Boston.

There are at present no definite plan...
"Hansel" into Boston, though Scott has said t...
...is of such ingenious self-contained construct...
...could be set up in any parking lot with an...
...outlet. Owners of such places should volunte...
...haps Caldwell should recall that there are...
...outlets in the Savoy, for in this "Hansel" she l...

G. SCHIRMER'S COLLECTION OF OPERAS.

HÄNSEL and GRETEL

Hänsel und Gretel

A FAIRY OPERA

IN THREE ACTS BY
ADELHEID WETTE

TRANSLATED AND ADAPTED INTO ENGLISH BY
CONSTANCE BACHE

THE MUSIC COMPOSED BY
E. HUMPERDINCK

COMPLETE VOCAL SCORE BY
R. KLEINMICHEL

G. SCHIRMER INC. NEW YORK.

ARGUMENT

ONCE upon a time a poor broom-maker and his wife lived in a lonesome cottage in the Harz Mountains with their little son, Hänsel, and daughter, Gretel. When our story opens, the father and mother have gone away to sell brooms in the neighboring villages, leaving the children at work in the house. But work is tiresome, especially when empty stomachs are clamoring for unattainable goodies; finally the youthful pair start to romping about the room, and at the height of their frolic the mother enters, weary from her long trip and unhappy because she has been unable to sell her wares. She scolds the children, and sends them out into the forest to pick wild strawberries for supper.—Late that evening the father returns, having disposed of his brooms at a good profit, and gaily unpacks a quantity of dainties; then, missing the children, he asks after them, and is horror-stricken at thought of their pitiful plight all alone after nightfall in the woods.

Act II discovers the children roaming through the woods, gradually filling their baskets with strawberries; heedless of direction and time, eventide finds them bewildered in the darkening forest haunted, as they have been taught to believe, by fairies and witches. The steep, rocky bulk of the Ilsenstein, a reputed gathering-place for evil sprites, looms up amid the trees; the wind whispers and moans uncannily, and shadowy bush and hollow take on strange and fearful shapes. The frightened children cower together beneath a spreading tree, and repeat their usual bedtime prayer to the "fourteen guardian angels," after which, calmer in spirit, they fall asleep with a fairy vision of the radiant angels floating around them.

Act III opens at daybreak; the children awake, refreshed by a good night's sleep, and sing merrily. All at once they notice an object overlooked in the evening darkness—a beautiful little house built of all manner of good things to eat, and giving off a most appetizing odor. This is, alas! the abode of a wicked witch, an ogress who entraps small boys and girls by her spells, pops them into her oven, and bakes them into delectable gingerbread, upon which she fares. Hänsel and Gretel approach the house and begin to break off tasty morsels from the walls; the witch appears and in due course casts a spell over them to prevent their escape; she now shuts Hänsel up in a sort of cage and feeds him on sweets to fatten him; then she tries to entice Gretel to bend down in front of the oven, so that she may be able to push her in and bake her; but Gretel pretends not to understand, and when the witch herself crossly bends down to show her how, the two children quickly shove her into the oven, bang the door shut, and dance around gleefully. Thereupon, all the gingerbread shapes that formed the hedge around the witch's house are transformed—her spell being broken—into their rightful shapes of happy boys and girls who thank Hänsel and Gretel for their deliverance; then the father and mother, who have been seeking their dear ones, burst upon the scene, and all winds up with a chorus of thanksgiving.

Hänsel and Gretel.

Dramatis Personæ.

Peter, a broom-maker.. *Baritone.*

Gertrude, his wife... *Mezzo-Soprano.*

Hänsel ⎫ .... *Mezzo-Soprano.*
Gretel ⎬ their children
       ⎭ .... *Soprano.*

The Witch who eats children.................................. *Mezzo-Soprano.*

Sandman (the sleep fairy)...*Soprano.*

Dewman (the dawn fairy).. *Soprano.*

Children...*Sopranos and Contraltos.*

Fourteen Angels...........................*Ballet.*

First Act.	Home.
Second Act.	The forest.
Third Act.	The witch's house.

Hänsel and Gretel.
Prelude.

Ruhige, nicht zu langsame Bewegung.
Andante con moto. (♩ = 69)

E. Humperdinck.

31957

Printed in the U. S. A.

6

31957

Das Zeitmass sehr allmählich beschleunigen.
Poco a poco accelerando.

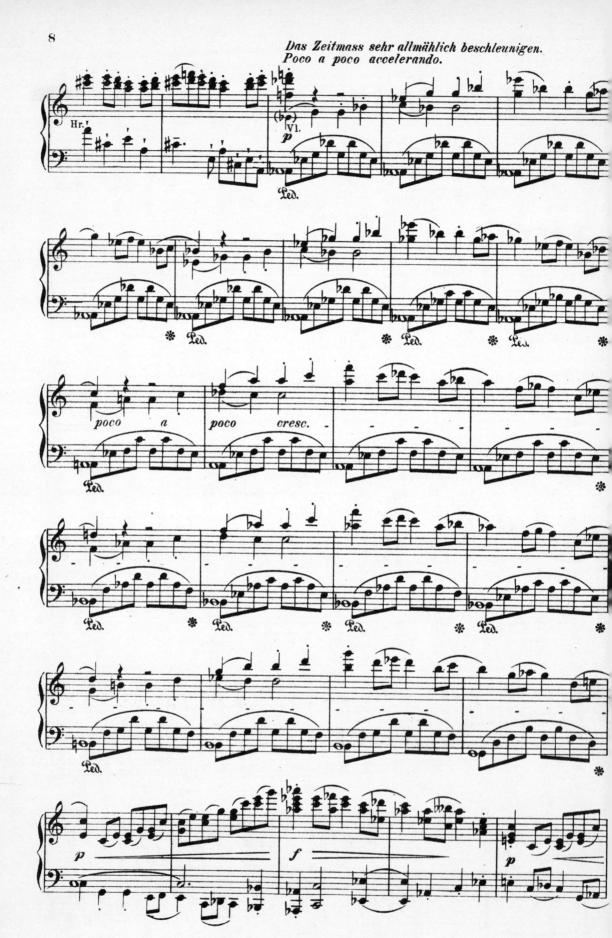

Im Zeitmass. *(Ein wenig zurückhaltend.)*
a tempo. *(un poco ritenuto.)*

First Act.

Home.

First Scene.

(A small and poorly furnished room. In the background a door; a small window near it, looking on to the forest. On the left a fireplace with chimney above it. On the walls are hanging brooms of various sizes. Hänsel is sitting by the door, making brooms, and Gretel opposite him by the fireplace, knitting a stocking.)

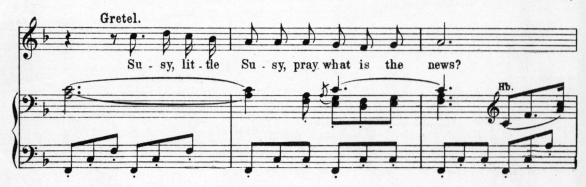

Gretel.

Su - sy, lit - tle Su - sy, pray what is the news?

Gretel (getting up.) ... Hänsel.

gain! Yes, I'm so hungry I don't know what to do! For weeks I've ea-ten nought but

slap table ... *walks anew toward Hansel*

Gretel.

Hush, Hän-sel, don't forget what father

bread, It's ve-ry hard,— it is in - deed!

sit

folds hands

said When mother too wished she were dead:___ "When past bear - ing

is our grief, God the Lord will send ____ re - lief!" *jumps up*

Hänsel.

Yes, yes, that

sounds all ve - ry fine, But a - las, off maxims we can - not dine! O

Gre - - tel, it would be such a treat If we had some-thing nice to

eat! Eggs and but-ter and su - et paste, I've al-most for - got - ten how they

poco ritard.

Gretel (stopping his mouth.)

Hush, don't give way to grumps,

taste— O Gretel, I wish—

Tempo.

Grow - ling and grumb - ling,   Full   of a - buse,   Off with you, Out with you.

Grow - ling and grumb - ling,   Full   of a - buse,   Off with you, Out with

cresc.

Shame on you, goose!   (pretending to sweep away.)   That's right!   Now

you, with you!

chaos brooms away

Hr.

f

f

Tempo primo. (♩ = ♪)

if you leave off com - plaining I'll   tell you a   most   de - light - - ful

Wind.

p   *f*   *p*   *dim.*

Bass.

I walks around front of table

Hänsel.

secret!   O   de - light - - ful!   it must be something

Hr.   Cl.   Fl.   Cl.   Fl.

p   *p*

Vcl.

20

Hänsel (dancing round the room.)

When blanc-mange is an-y-where near, Then Hän - sel, Hän - sel,

Hän-sel is there! How thick is the cream on the milk, let's

(He licks the cream off his finger.)

taste it! O Ge - mi - ni, wouldn't I like to

Più animato. *drops broom*
Gretel.

(gives him a rap on his fingers.)

What, Hän-sel, tast-ing? Aren't you a - shamed? Out with your

drink it!
Più animato.

suit me! It's such a bore! Dancing is jol-li-er far,—— I'm

sure!

Gretel.

Danc - ing! Danc - ing! O yes, that's bet - ter far.

And sing a song to keep us in time! One that our grand - mother

used to sing us: Sing then, and dance in time to the sing - ing!

24

Gretel.

So that I may dance like you. With your foot you tap tap tap,

With your hand you clap clap clap, Right foot first, Left foot then, Round about and

Hänsel.

back a-gain! With your foot you tap tap tap, With your hand you clap clap clap,

Gretel.

O I'm sure you'll soon succeed! Try a-gain and I can see Hän-sel soon will

(clapping her hands joyfully.)

dance like me! With your head you nick nick nick, With your fingers you

click click click, Right foot first, Left foot then, Round a-bout and back a-gain!

"G. turns H. around and pushes him / he falls down!"

(then gives him a push.)

la la la la la la la! Come and have a twirl, my dear-est Hän-sel. Come and have a

G. beckens

turn with me, I pray, Come here to me, come here to me, I'm sure you can't say

Hänsel (gruffly.)

Nay! Go a-way from me, go a-way from me, I'm much too proud for you! With

Gretel.

lit - le girls I do not dance, And so, my dear, a-dieu! Go,

poco ritard.   Tempo.   (dances round Hänsel)

stu - pid Hans, con - cei - ted Hans, you'll see I'll make you dance! Tra la la la la la la la

dance together man style

as before — — — — — — — and gives him a push.)

la la la, tra la la la la la la la la! Come and have a twirl, my dear-est

Hänsel (dances round Gretel.)

Tra la la la la la la la

H. steps on G. toe G. grabs foot

Hän-sel, Come and have a turn with me, I pray,

la la la, tra la la la la la la la la! O Gre-tel dear, O

Gretel.

sis-ter dear, Your stocking has a hole! O Hän-sel dear, O bro-ther dear, D'you

take me for a fool? With naugh-ty boys I do not dance, And so, my dear, a-

H. pulls g. hair

Hänsel. *poco ritard.* *Tempo.* Gretel.

dieu! Now don't be cross, you sil-ly goose, You'll see I'll make you dance! Tra la

H. runs to chair & G. dances around him

(they dance as before) la tra la la tra la la la la, tra la la tra la la tra la la! Come and have a

Hänsel.

Tra la

H. pushes chair away *Hold*

twirl, my dear-est Hän-sel, Come and have a turn, my dear-est Hans! Sing

la tra la la tra la la la la, tra la la tra la la tra la la! Sing

hands—turn around   stop   Y. points to stockings

lu-sti-ly hur-rah, hur-rah!   While I dance with you!   And if the stockings

lu-sti-ly hur-rah, hur-rah!   While I dance with you!   And if the shoes are

(They dance by turns as before.)

are in holes, Why   mother'll knit some new!   Come and have a

all in holes, Why   mother ll buy some new!   Trala   la trala la tra la   la la la,   tra la

Y. takes front of chair   Han

play Horsie around table

twirl, my   dear-est   Hän-sel!   On-ly have a

la tra la la tra la   la!   Tra la   la tra la la tra la   la la la,   tra la

back

(Then they seize each other's hands and dance round and round,

twirl, my dear-est Hänsel! Tra la   la tra la la, tra la   la tra la la.   tra la

la trala la trala   la la la, tra la   la la   la, tra la   la la   la,   tra la

quicker and quicker, until at last they lose their balance and tumble over one another onto the floor.)

la   tra la la,   trala   la   trala la,   trala la trala la,   trala la trala la,   tra

la   la   la,   trala   la   trala la,   tra   la trala la,   trala la trala la,   tra

la!

la!

drop it. Hsch on opposite side of stage.

Scene II.

Allegro.

The Mother.

Hal-lo!

Gretel.

(At this moment the door opens; the children see their mother coming and jump up quickly.)

Here's mother!

Hänsel.

Heav-ens, here's mother!

Allegro.

fp *cresc.* *f*

The Mother.

What _____ is all this dis-turb - ance?

riten. 8 Fl.

ff *ff*

Tempo primo.

Gretel.

(Embarrassment.)

'Twas Hänsel _ he wanted _

Hänsel.

'Twas Gretel _ she said I _

Tempo primo.

Ten.

p Vcl

36

children, And make your id - le fing - ers ting - le!

Vl.

p   *cresc. - - - -*   *fp*

(In her anger at the children she gives the milkjug a knock, which sends it clattering on to the floor.)

fp   *cresc. - - -*   *ff*

Gra-cious! There goes the jug all to pie-ces!

dimin.   *f*

(weeping)   (She looks at her skirt, down which

What now can I cook for sup-per?

Hb.

dimin. - -   *pp*

38

bring the bas-ket brim-ful I'll whip_ you so that you'll

both _____ run a - way!

(The children run into the forest.)

(She sits down by the table, exhausted.)

No crust in the cup-board   No milk in the pot,

(She rests her head on her hand.)

No, no-thing but wa-ter to drink!—

Wea-ry am I,   weary   of liv-ing!

(Lays her head down on her arms and drops asleep.)

Father,   send— help—   to me!—

Scene III.

purse, And in the sto-mach an e-ven worse. Tra la la la, tra la la

la, Hun - ger is the poor man's curse! Tra la la, tra la la la

(The father appears at the window, and

la, Hun - ger is the poor man's curse!

during the following he comes into the room in a very lively mood, with a basket on his back.)

2.'Tis-n't much that we re - quire, Just a lit-tle food and
3.Yes, the rich en-joys his din-ner,While the poor grows dai - ly

fire! But a-las, it's true e - nough, Life on some of us is
thin-ner;Strives to eat, as well he may, Some-what less than yes-ter-

rit.
(complaining) *Tempo*.

rough! Tra la la la, tra la la la, Hun - ger is a cus-tom-er
day! Tra la la la, tra la la la, Hun - ger is the de-vil to

tough! Tra la la, tra la la la la, Hun - ger is a cus-tom-er
pay! Tra la la, tra la la la la, Hun - ger is the de-vil to

46

Father.

With - in my breast Cal-led so for food I could not

rest! Tra la la, tra la la la, Hun - ger is an ur-gent

beast, Tra la la, tra la la la la, Pinch - es, gnaws, and gives no

Mother.

So, so! And this wild beast,

48

Come prima.

spare!

Father.

Tra la la la, tra la la la, cheer up, mo - ther, for here am I,

Come prima.

Bringing luck and jol - li - ty!

(he takes his basket and begins to display the contents.)

Look, mother! doesn't all this

Mother.

Man, man, what

food please you?

Tempo come prima.

53

meanwhile packs away the things, lights a fire, breaks eggs into a saucepan, etc.)

Yon - der to the town I went, There was to be a great e - -vent,

Weddings, fairs and pre - pa - ra - tion For all kinds of ju - bi - la - tion!

Now's my chance to do some sel - ling,

So for that you may be thank - ful! He who

wants a feast to keep, He must scrub and brush and sweep,

54

31957

(He knocks down some tinpots off the chimneypiece with a clatter.)

Now make haste with cup and plat-ter, Bring the glass-es, bring the ket-tle:

Mother.

Here's a health to the be-som-

Here's a health to the be- - som-

ma - ker! (He puts the glass of toddy to his lips, but suddenly stops short.)

ma - ker! But stay, why, where are the children?

(Shrugs her shoulders with a puzzled air.)

Gone with Hans? Oh!

Hänsel, Gre-tel, what's gone with Hans?

Un poco più animato.

60

63

stalks a - round with a crinch - ing, crunch - ing, munch - ing sound, and

children plump and tender to eat she lures with ma - gic ginger-bread sweet.

Un poco più animato.

On e - - vil bent, with

fell intent she lures the chil - dren, poor little things, in the

(wringing her hands)

For the ogress?　　O horror!　　Heav'n help us! the

served up for dinner!　　For the ogress!

(runs out of the house.)

children! O what shall we do!

Hi,　　mother, mother,

(takes the whisky bottle from the table and runs after her.)

wait for me!　　We'll both go to - gether the witch to seek!

Wind.

(The curtain falls quickly.)

(Prelude to the 2ⁿᵈ Act)

✠ Goes on to the "Witches' Ride."

The Witches' Ride.

Prelude to second Act.

68

Poco a poco più animato.

70

Un poco più tranquillo.

(The curtain rises.)

Molto tranquillo.

(The middle of the forest. In the background

is the "Ilsenstein", thickly surrounded by fir-trees. On the right is a large fir-tree, under which Gretel is sitting on a mossy tree-trunk, and making a garland of wild roses. By her side lies a nosgay of flowers. Amongst the bushes on the left is Hänsel, looking for strawberries. Sunset.)

Second Act.
In the forest.
Scene I.

Molto tranquillo. (♩ = 66)

Gretel (humming quietly to herself.)

There stands a lit - tle man in the wood a - lone, He wears a lit - tle man - tle of vel - vet brown, Say who can the mankin be, Standing there be-neath the tree, With the lit - tle man - tle of vel - vet brown? His hair is all of

gold, and his cheeks are red, He wears a lit - tle black cap up - on his

head, Say who can the mankin be, Standing there so si - lently, With the little

(She holds up the garland of roses and looks it all round)

black cap up - on his head?

With the little black cap up - on his

(puts the wreath on her.)

It is on-ly fit for a girl!

Ha, Gre-tel,

fine feathers! O the deuce! Now you shall be Queen of the

Gretel.

If I'm to be Queen of the wood, Then I must have the nose - gay

wood!

too!

Hänsel (gives her the nosegay.)

Queen of the wood, with scep-tre and

crown, I give you the strawberries, but don't ____ eat them

poco riten.

all!

Tempo.

(He gives the basketful of strawberries into her other hand, at the same time kneeling before her

in homage.)

Gretel (roguishly.)

Cuckoo, cuckoo, where are you?

(At this moment a cuckoo is heard.) **Hänsel** (pointing with his hand.)

Cuckoo, cuckoo, how are you?

Cuckoo-instrument (behind the scenes, heard as if quite in the distance.)

(takes a strawberry from the basket, and pokes it into Hänsel's mouth: he sucks it up as though he were drinking an egg.)

Hänsel (springing up.)

O - ho! I can do that just like you!

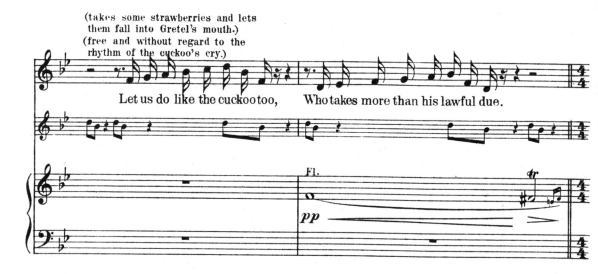

(takes some strawberries and lets them fall into Gretel's mouth.)
(free and without regard to the rhythm of the cuckoo's cry.)

Let us do like the cuckoo too, Who takes more than his lawful due.

(It begins to grow dusk.)

Gretel (does the same.)

Cuckoo, where are you?

Hänsel (helping himself again.)

Cuckoo, how are you?

80

81

Know you what the fo - - rest says?

molto espressivo

"Chil - dren, chil - dren," it says, "are you not____ a - fraid?"

Solo - Violin.

(Hänsel spies all round uneasily.)

(At last he turns in despair to Gretel.) **Hänsel.**

Gre - tel,

86

31957

(A thick mist rises and completely hides the background.)

(Rushes horror-struck under the tree and falls on her knees, hiding herself behind Hänsel.)

Scene II.

Moderato.

Sand-man (the Sleep-Fairy: strewing sand in the children's eyes.)
(with a soft gentle voice)

I shut the children's peep — ers, sh! And guard the lit - tle

sleep — ers, sh! For dear - ly do I love them, sh! And glad - ly watch a -

bove them, sh! And with my lit - tle bag of sand By

ev' - ry child's bed - side I stand; Then lit - tle tir - ed

sempre p

Two are on my left hand, Two who warmly cov - er, Two who o'er me

sempre p

right hand, Two are on my left hand, Two who warmly cov - er,

Fl.

pp subito

cresc.

poco rit.

hov - er, Two to whom tis giv - en To guide my steps to Hea - -

Two who o'er me hov - - er, Two who guide my steps to Hea - -

poco rit.

Vl.

Tempo.

ven.   (They sink down on the moss, and go to sleep with their arms twined round each other.)

ven.

Tempo.

Wind.

pp

Vcl.

Ped.   *

poco ritard.

Ped.   *   Ped.   *   Ped.   *

(Complete darkness.)

(Here a bright light

suddenly breaks through the mist,   which forthwith rolls itself together into the form of a

Con espressione.

staircase vanishing in perspective in the middle of the stage.)

Scene III.

Pantomime.

Poco a poco più animato.

(Fourteen angels, in light floating garments, pass down the staircase two and two,   at

intervals, while it is getting gradually lighter. The angels place themselves, according to the order mentioned in the evening hymn, around the sleeping children; the first couple at their heads,

the second at their feet, the third on the right, the fourth on the left; then the fifth and sixth couples

distribute themselves amongst the other couples so that the circle of the angels is completed.)

(Lastly the seventh couple comes into the circle, and takes its place as "guardian angels" on each side of the children.)

(The remaining angels now join hands and dance a stately dance around the group.)

Tempo moderato.

(The whole stage is filled with an intense light.)

(Whilst the angels group themselves in a picturesque tableau the curtain slowly falls.)

Third Act.
The Witch's House.

(Scene the same as at the end of Act II. The background is still hidden in mist, which gradually rises during the following. The angels have vanished. Morning is breaking. The Dew-Fairy steps forward and shakes dewdrops from a blue-bell over the sleeping children.)

la - zy, ding! dong! ding!

dong! And with the golden light of day I chase the fa - ding

night a - way, Fresh dew around me sha - king, And hill and dale a -

wa - king; Then up, with all your pow - ers En - joy the morning

hours,— The scent of trees and flow-ers, Then up, ye sleep-ers a-

wa- -ken! The ro-sy dawn is smi-

sempre con Ped.

ling, Then up, ye sleep-ers, a- wake,————— a- -

cresc. *dimin.*

(Hurries off singing. The children begin to stir.)

wake!

Un poco più lento.

Gretel (rubs her eyes, looks around her, and raises herself a little, whilst Hänsel turns over on the oth
side to go to sleep again.)

Where am I? Wa - king? Or do I dream?

How come I in the wood to lie?

High in the

branch - es I hear a gentle twittering, Birds are be-

gin - ning to sing so sweet - - ly; From ear - ly

dawn they are all a - wake, And war - ble their morning hymn

— of grate - ful praise. Dear lit - tle sing - ers, lit - - tle

sing - ers, Good morn - ing!

(turns to Hänsel.)

Ti-re-li-re-li, ti-re-li-re-li, ti-re-li-re-li, ti-re-li-re-li,

cresc.

ti - ti - ti - ti-re-li-ti, ti-re-li-ti, ti-re-li, ti-re-li-reli-

mf

li, ti-re-li-re-li-re - li-ti - ti - ti - ti -

p

cresc.

- ti - ti - - ti!

Hänsel (suddenly jumps up with a start)

Ki - ke-ri - ki! it's ear-ly yet! Ki - ke-ri -

Vl.   Fl.

f   p

110

float - ing in the dis - tance a - way.

Sud-den — all a - round a light was streaming, Rays of glo-ry from

Hea - ven beam-ing, And a gol - den lad - der

saw I des-cend - ing, An - gels a - down it glid-ing,

Such love - ly an - gels with shi - - ning gol-den wings.

114

Gretel (astonished)
And did you al-so be-hold all this?

Hänsel (interrupting her quickly.)
Fourteen angels there must have been!

Un poco ritardando.
Hänsel.
Truly, 'twas wondrous fair! And upward I saw them

Scene II.

(He turns towards the background: at this moment the last remains of the mist clear away. In place of the fir-trees is seen the Witch's House at the Ilsenstein, shining in the rays of the rising sun. A little distance off, to the left, is an oven; opposite this, on the right, a large cage, both joined to the witch's house by a fence of gingerbread figures.)

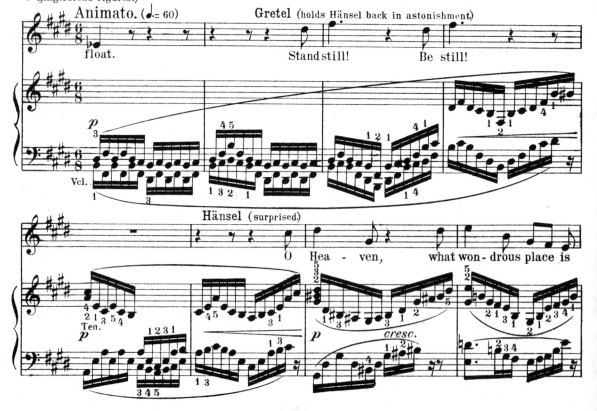

Animato. (♩.= 60)
float.

Gretel (holds Hänsel back in astonishment)
Stand still! Be still!

Hänsel (surprised)
O Hea - ven, what won-drous place is

(in the greatest excitement)

this,   As ne'er in all my

life_____ have I seen!

(Both gaze at the house spellbound)

Un poco più tranquillo.

Gretel (gradually regains her self-possession.)

What o - dour de-li-cious, O

gin - ger - bread hedge! __

gin - ger - bread hedge! __

cresc.

O ma - - - gic

O ma - - - gic

Wind.

Hr.

p

cas - - tle, how nice you'd be to eat! __ Where

cas - - tle, how nice you'd be to eat! __ Where

Hb.

Vl.

hides the prin - cess __ who en - joys so great a

hides the prin - cess __ who en - joys so great a

p

118

31957

to din - ner there, _____ to din - ner

to din - ner there, _____ to din - ner

there, _____ to din - ner there!

there, _____ to din - ner there!

Hänsel.   (resolutely)

No sound I hear,   No, nothing is stirring!   Come, let's go in-

like _____ two mice _____ per - se - ve - -ring!

_____ two mice _____ per - se - ve - -ring!

Hb..

cresc. - - - - -

Fl.

Vl.

f

(They hop along, hand in hand, towards the back of the stage; -

Trp.

ff

then stand still, -

Hr.

f

dim. - - -

and then steal along cautiously on tip-toe to the house. After some hesi-

p

più p

Vcl.

tation Hänsel breaks off a bit of cake from the right-hand corner.)

Scene III.

(He breaks a big piece of cake off the wall.)

Allegro non troppo.

These dain-ty mor-sels I'm real-ly gloating on,
And you, my

lit — tle maid — en, I'm dot-ing on!

Un poco più tranquillo.

Come, lit-tle mou-sey, Come in-to my hou-sey!

Come with me, my pre-cious, I'll give you sweetmeats de-li-cious!

134

bliss! Come, lit-tle mou-sey, Come in-to my hou-sey!

Cl.

p dolce

Gretel. f

But say, what will you

Come with me, my precious, I'll give you sweetmeats de - li - cious!

Vcl.

Gretel. The Witch.

with my bro-ther do? Well, well—— I'll feed and fat-ten him up well,

Hb.

Ten.

p

Fl.

p

mf

Cl.

espressivo

Hr.
Bass.

With ev' - ry sort of dainty de - li-cious, To make him tender and

Cr. ingl.

not.

The Witch. What is the great treat in store for me?

The Witch. What?

dimin. - - - - *p* Cl. *mf* Hb. Str.

The Witch. Yes, my dear children, hearing and sight

Fl. Vcl. *p* *p* Hr.

Hänsel. In this great pleasure will dis-appear quite! Eh? both my hearing and see-ing are good! You'd

Cl. Hb. *p* Vcl. *p dolce* Hr. Bcl.

(resolutely)
bet-ter take care you do me no harm! Gre-tel, trust not her flat-ter-ing words,

Vl. cresc. *f*

138

(He has in the meantime got out of the rope, and runs with Gretel to the foreground.)

Come, sis-ter, come, let's run a-way!

(Here they are stopped by the Witch, who imperiously raises against them both a stick which hangs at her girdle, with repeated gestures of spell-binding.)

The Witch.

Hold!

(the stage becomes gradually darker.)

Ho-cus po-cus, witches' charm! Move not, as you

fear my arm! Back or forward do not try,

139

140

Hän-sel's growing fat and nice. We'll feed him up, you'll see my

rea-son, And with sweet al-monds andwithrai-sins sea-son. I'll go in-

doors, the things to pre-pare, And you remain here where you

(She grins as she holds up her finger warningly, and goes into the house.) Gretel (stiff and motionless.)

are! O, what a horrid

Un poco più animato.

Più animato.

Allegro.
(Gretel moves again.)

Ri-gid bo-dy loosen, hush! Now up and move again.

bright and blithesome, limbs all be-come a-gain sup-ple and lithesome! Go my pop-pet,

go my pet, You the ta — ble now shall set: Lit-tle knife, lit-tle fork,

lit-tle dish, lit-tle plate, Lit-tle ser-viette for my lit-tle mate!

Now get ev'-ry-thing rea-dy and nice, Or else ___ I shall

lock you up too in a trice! He he he he he he!

(She threatens and titters. Gretel hurries off.)

Molto più lento.

(To Hänsel who pretends to be asleep.)

The fool is slumb'-ring, it does seem

queer How youth can sleep and have ___ no fear! Well, sleep a-

way, you sim - ple sheep,___ Soon you will sleep your

last___ long sleep!___

But first with Gre - tel I'll be - gin, Off

you, dear maid - en, I will dine;___ You're so ten - der, plump and

148

(She pushes a couple more faggots under; the fire flames up and then dies down again.)

The Witch (rubbing her hands with glee.)

Yes, Gre-tel mine, how well off you I'll dine!

See, see, O how sly!____

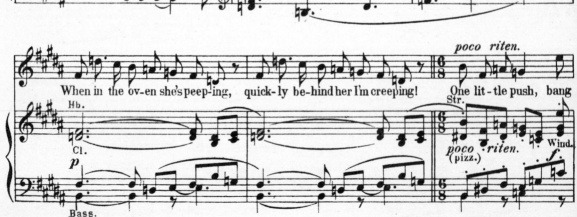

When in the ov-en she's peep-ing, quick-ly be-hind her I'm creeping! One lit-tle push, bang

L'istesso tempo. (♪=♪)

(In her wild delight she seizes a broomstick and begins to ride upon it.)

So hop,hop,hop, gal-lop, lop, lop! My broom-stick nag, come do not lag!

(She rides excitedly round on the broomstick.)

At dawn of day I ride a-way, An

(She rides again; Gretel meanwhile is watching at the window.)

here and there and ev'- ry-where!

At mid-night hour, when none can know, to join the witch-es' dance I go!

And three and four Are witch-es' lore, And five and six Are witch-es' tricks, And nine is one, And ten is none, And seven is nil, Or what she will! And thus they ride till dawn of day!

152

(Hopping madly along she rides to the back of the stage, and vanishes for a time behind the cottage.)

comes visible again; she comes to the foreground, ———

where she suddenly pulls up — — — — — — — — — — — and dismounts.)

153

154

(Hänsel pokes out a small bone.)

Ge - mi - ni! O -

ho! O how scraggy, how lean!

Ur - chin, you're a scraggy one, As bad ___

___ as a ske-le-ton!

The Witch (calls.)

Mai-den! Gre-tel! (Gretel appears at the door.)

156

not Gretel, then will be Just done to a T!

(Hänsel and Gretel fall joyfully into one another's arms.)

The Witch Valse.

Un poco meno mosso. (♩ = ♪)

Hur - rah! Now sing the

witch is dead, Real - ly dead, No more to dread!___ Hur - rah!

Now sing the witch is still, Death-ly still, We___ can eat our fill! Now all the

(They seize each

spell is o'er, Real-ly o'er, We fear no more!____ Yes ____ let us

spell is o'er, Real-ly o'er, We fear no more!____ Yes ____ let us

a tempo

other's hands.)

hap-py be, Dancing so mer-ri-ly; Now the old witch is gone, We'll have no end of fun!

hap-py be, Dancing so mer-ri-ly; Now the old witch is gone, We'll have no end of fun!

Hey!____ hur-rah, hur-rah! Hip hur-rah! Hip hur-

Hey!____ hur-rah, hur-rah! Hip hur-rah! Hip hur-

cresc.

(They take each other round the waist and waltz

rah!____ Hur-rah!____

rah!____ Hur-rah!____

together, first in the front of the stage, and then gradually in the direction of the Witch's house.)

(When they get there Hänsel breaks loose from Gretel and rushes into the house, shutting the door after

him. Then from the upper window he throws down apples, pears, oranges, gilded nuts, and all kinds of

sweetmeats into Gretel's outstretched apron.)

(Meanwhile the oven begins crackling loudly, and the flames burn high. Then there is a loud crash, and

the oven falls thundering into bits.)

(Hänsel and Gretel, who in their terror let their sweetmeats all

fall down, hurry towards the oven startled, and stand there motionless. Their astonishment increases when

they become aware of a troop of children around them, whose disguise of cakes has fallen from them.)

Gretel. (spoken) There, see those little children dear,
Hänsel. I wonder how they all came here!

Scene IV.

166

yet you're singing   too!

sempre pp

O   touch   us, we

sempre pp

O   touch   us, we

pp

Ped.   *   Ped.

Hänsel (embarrassed.)

O   touch   them fo

pray,   that   we   may   all   a - wake!

pray,   that   we   may   all   a - wake!

m.s.   *m.s.*

Ped.

Gretel.

Yes,   let   me stroke this   in - nocent face!

me,   I   dare   not try!

*   Ped.   *   Ped.   *   Ped.   *

(She caresses the nearest child, who opens its eyes and smiles.)

O touch me too, O touch me too, that

O touch me too, O touch me too, that

cresc.

I____ al - so may a - wake!

I____ al - so may a - wake!

(Gretel goes and caresses all the rest of the children, who open their eyes and smile, without moving. meanwhile Hänsel seizes the juniper - branch.)

Poco a poco accelerando sin' al _ _ _ _ _

cresc. _

Hänsel.

Ho - cus po - cus el - derbush! Ri - gid bo - dy loosen, hush!

mf

più cresc.

168

169

hands to - ge - ther while we sing! _____ Then

hands to - ge - ther while we sing! Then sing and spring, then dance and sing, For

sing and spring, then dance and sing, That through the wood our song of praise may

cakes and all good things we bring, That through the wood our song of praise may

sound, ____ and e - cho re - peat it all a - round! ____

sound, and e - cho re - peat it all a - round; all a - round! ____

who have watched o'er our steps and led them right, You we praise and

who have watched o'er our steps and led them right, _____ We

Single.

We thank you both _____

thank you both for all our joy and won-drous de-light!

thank for all our joy and won-drous de-light, _____

praise _____ and thank, _____ we praise and thank _____ for all our

_____ for all our joy _____ and won-drous de-light, _____ for all our

We thank you both _____ for all our won-drous de-light! We

173

25788

174

(The Father appears in the background with the Mother, and stops when he sees the children.)
(half spoken)

Tra la la la, tra la la la la, Ha! Why they're really there!

Vivo.

dimin.

Last Scene.

Hänsel. (running towards them.)

Fa - ther! Mo - ther!

Allegro molto. (♩=120)

Hr.

Gretel. (the same.)   Mother.   Father.

Fa - ther! Mo - ther! Chil - dren dear! O

cre

(Joyful embracing.)

wel - come, poor chil - dren in - no - cent!

scen - do ff

(Meanwhile two of the boys have dragged the Witch, in the form of a big gingerbread cake, out of the

Un poco

ruins of the oven. At the sight of her they all burst into a shout of joy. The boys place the Witch in the

All.

Ha!

Meno mosso. ($\mathbf{d}$=104)

Hr.

ff

ff

middle of the stage.)

f dimin.

Father.

Hb.

p

Chil - dren, see the won - der wrought, How the witch her - self was caught,

Un - a - ware, In the snare Laid for you with cun - ning

Fl.

cresc.

All the rest.

See, O see the won-der wrought, How the witch her-self was caught, rare!

Un-a-ware In the snare Laid for us with cun - ning

(The two boys drag the Witch into the cottage.)

rare!

Such is Heaven's chastisement, E - vil works will have an end.

Poco a poco più allargando. *riten.*

When past bearing is our grief, God the Lord will send us sure re - lief! Yes,

When past bearing is our grief, God the Lord will send ____ re -

Wind.

Vd.

Maestoso.

Gretel.
When past bear-ing is our grief, God the Lord will

Hansel.
When past bear-ing is our grief, God the Lord will

Mother.
When past bear-ing is our grief, God the Lord will

Father.
lief! God the Lord will

When past bear-ing is our grief, God the Lord will

When past bear-ing is our grief, God the Lord will

Maestoso.

Più allargando.
molto cresc.

cresc.

(Whilst the children dance in a joyous
circle round the group, the curtain falls.)

The End.